The Gree

Jill

Illustrated by Teri Gower

Snap!

The leaves of Mum's new plant snapped shut.

Snap!

"What's it called?" asked Charlotte.

"I think it's a Venus Fly Trap," said Mum.

Snap! went the Venus Fly Trap.

"Why does it keep doing that?" asked Charlotte.

"It's probably hungry," said Mum.

"What does a Venus Fly Trap eat?" asked Charlotte.

"Flies!" said Mum.

Snap! went the Venus Fly Trap hungrily.

Mum put the plant on the kitchen
window sill. She stirred the stew.

"Dinner's ready," she said and
went to fetch the baby.

Slurp! Snap!

Mum put the baby in his high chair. Charlotte sat up to the table. Mum looked in the saucepan. It was empty.

"What's happened to the stew?" asked Mum.

They looked everywhere for the stew, but they could not find it.

Charlotte looked at Mum's plant.

Was that gravy in the corner of its jaws? Had the plant eaten the stew?

Snap! it went. *Gurgle! Gurgle! Snap!*

"Do Venus Fly Traps eat flies and stew?" thought Charlotte.

The door bell rang. Mum gave the
baby his rattle then went to the door.
Scrunch! Snap!

"Mamamamama," cried the baby.

Mum came running back.

"What's happened to the rattle?" asked Mum.

They looked everywhere for the rattle, but they could not find it.

9

Charlotte looked at Mum's plant.

Was that the baby's rattle sticking out of its jaws? Had the plant eaten the rattle?

Snap! it went. *Rattle! Rattle! Rattle! Snap!*

"Do Venus Fly Traps eat flies, stew and rattles?" thought Charlotte.

The telephone rang. Mum went to answer it.

Scring! Snap!

"What's happened to the
telephone?" asked Mum.

They looked everywhere for the
telephone, but they could not find it.

Charlotte looked at Mum's plant.

Was that the telephone wire in the corner of its jaws? Had the plant eaten the telephone?

Snap! it went. *Ring! Ring! Snap!*

"Do Venus Fly Traps eat flies, stew, rattles and telephones?" thought Charlotte. "I think it probably eats everything," she thought, "so it can't be a Venus Fly Trap at all."

The next day, there was a flower show in town.

"I'm going to enter my plant for the 'Fantastic Plants' class," said Mum.

"I'd better keep an eye on it," thought Charlotte.

Mum's plant was put on a table with lots of other plants.

"Look out!" said Charlotte.

Squilch! Snap! One of the plants disappeared.

"Now there will be trouble!" thought Charlotte.

16

"You stole my plant!" someone shouted.

Squelch! Snap!

"No! You stole mine!" yelled another.

Squilch! Squelch! Snap!

One by one, the plants on the table disappeared. The people became angrier and angrier.

Charlotte ran to find Mum and the baby. They were looking at a big silver cup on the judge's table.

"Come quickly," said Charlotte. "Your plant's eating all the other plants."

"Don't be silly!" said Mum. But they went back to the 'Fantastic Plants' table.

There was only one plant left. It was enormous! Leaves poked out from the corners of its big jaws.

Had it gobbled up all the others?

Snap! it went. *Munch! Crunch! Snap!*

"Oh dear!" said Mum. "We'd better take it home."

But the plant had grown so heavy that she couldn't lift it.

The judge came along the path.

He was carrying the big silver cup.

The mayor came along behind him.

He was wearing a big gold chain.

"Look out!" said Charlotte again.

Too late! The plant reached out its jaws on a long hairy neck. It opened those jaws wide.

Snap!

Before anyone could stop it, it had eaten the big silver cup …

Snap!

… and the big gold chain.

A lady rushed over to the table.

"How wonderful!" she cried. "I've been looking for one of these plants all my life!"

"Haven't you seen a Venus Fly Trap before?" asked Mum.

"This isn't a Venus Fly Trap!" said the lady. "It's a Greedy Snapjaw."

Charlotte giggled.

"But what are we going to do with
a Greedy Snapjaw?" cried the judge.
"I have an idea," said the mayor.

A lorry soon arrived. A crane lifted the Greedy Snapjaw onto the lorry.

Snap! it went.

Charlotte felt sad to see it go.

"Don't worry," said the mayor.
"You can come and see it
tomorrow."

The next morning, they drove to the rubbish tip. Charlotte saw the bottle bank, the newspaper bank, the can bank and the plastic bank. In the middle of them all was the plant.

A big notice said:

**THE GREEDY SNAPJAW
RUBBISH EATER**

Recycle what you can.
This plant will eat
everything else.

Charlotte looked at the Greedy Snapjaw. Its jaws were smiling and its leaves waved at her. She waved back. She was pleased that it was happy. She watched it being fed.

Snap!

People came from far and wide with their rubbish to feed the Greedy Snapjaw.

Slurp! Scrunch! Squilch! Squelch! Snap!

Charlotte had been right. The Greedy Snapjaw would eat ... well ... everything!

Snap!